It's Easy To Play Oasis.

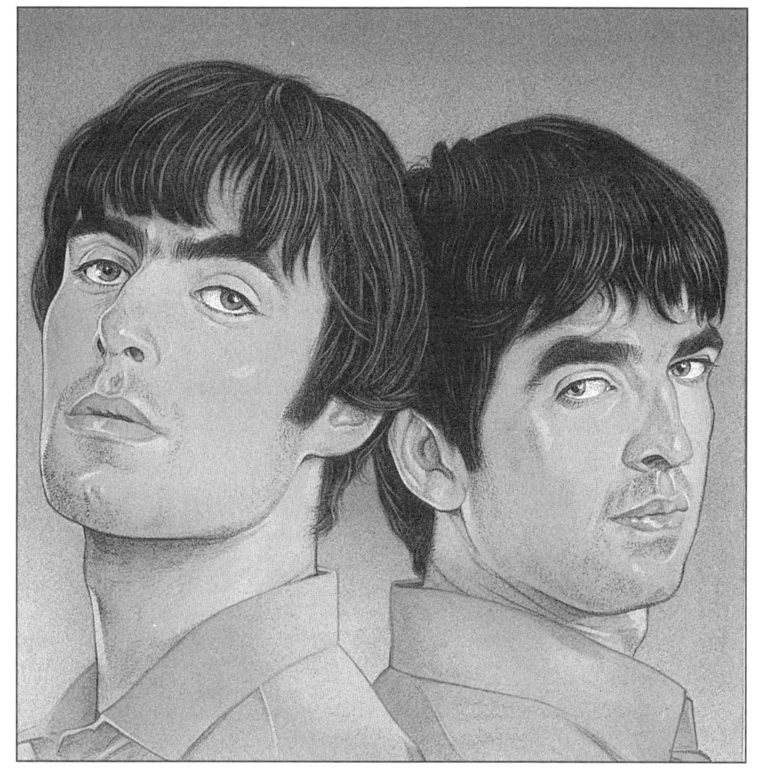

Wise Publications
London / New York / Paris / Sydney / Copenhagen / Madrid

Exclusive Distributors:

Music Sales Limited
8/9 Frith Street,
London W1V 5TZ, England.

Music Sales Pty Limited
120 Rothschild Avenue,
Rosebery, NSW 2018, Australia.

Order No. AM936276
ISBN 0-7119-5647-2

Art direction by Michael Bell Design.
Cover illustration by Mark Thomas.
Compiled by Peter Evans.
Music arranged by Stephen Duro.
Music processed by Allegro Reproductions.

Printed in the United Kingdom by
Caligraving Limited, Thetford, Norfolk.

Champagne Supernova

Words & Music by Noel Gallagher

B♭/F
B♭
B♭/A♭
sky. Some day you will find me caught be - neath the land - slide in a
B♭/G
B♭/F
cham - pagne su - per - no - va, a cham - pagne su - per - no - va in the
B♭
B♭/A♭
B♭/G
B♭
sky.
B♭
B♭/A♭
1. Wake up the dawn and ask her why, a dream - er dreams she nev - er dies,
(Verse 2 see block lyric)
B♭/G
B♭/F
B♭
wipe that tear a - way now from your eyes. Slow - ly walk - ing down the hall,

B♭/A♭
fast - er than a can - non ball,
B♭/G
where were you while we were get - ting high?
F
Some day you will
B♭
find me caught be - neath the
B♭/A♭
land - slide, in a
B♭/G
cham - pagne su - per - no - va in the
B♭/F
sky.
Some day you will
B♭
find me caught be - neath the
B♭/A♭
land - slide, in a
B♭/G
cham - pagne su - per - no - va, a
F
cham - pagne su - per - no - va. 'Cause
E♭
peo - ple be - lieve that they're
gon - na get a - way for the sum
B♭
- mer

A♭
E♭
but you and I we live and die, the world's still spin - ning round, we don't know

F
F7
B♭
B♭/A♭
why, why, why, why, why.

B♭/G
1.
B♭/F
2.
B♭/F

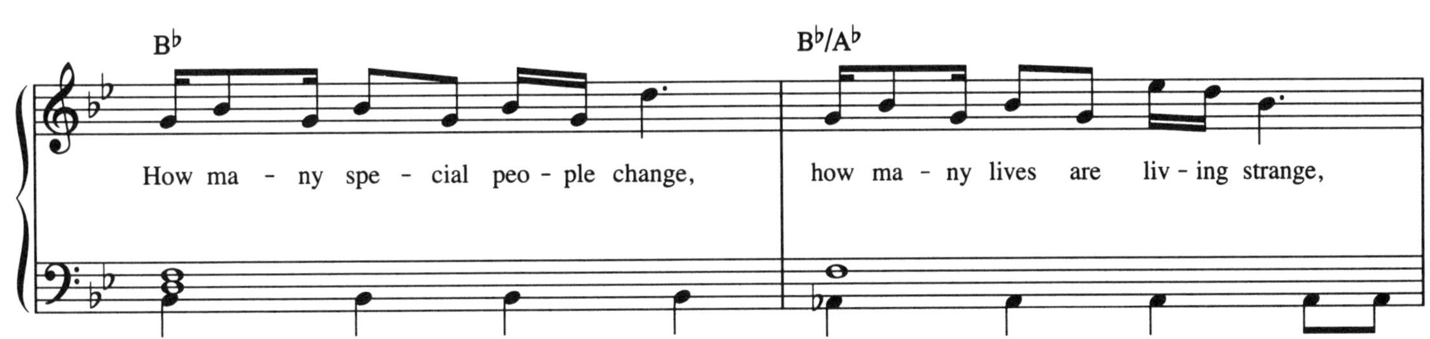
B♭
B♭/A♭
How ma - ny spe - cial peo - ple change, how ma - ny lives are liv - ing strange,

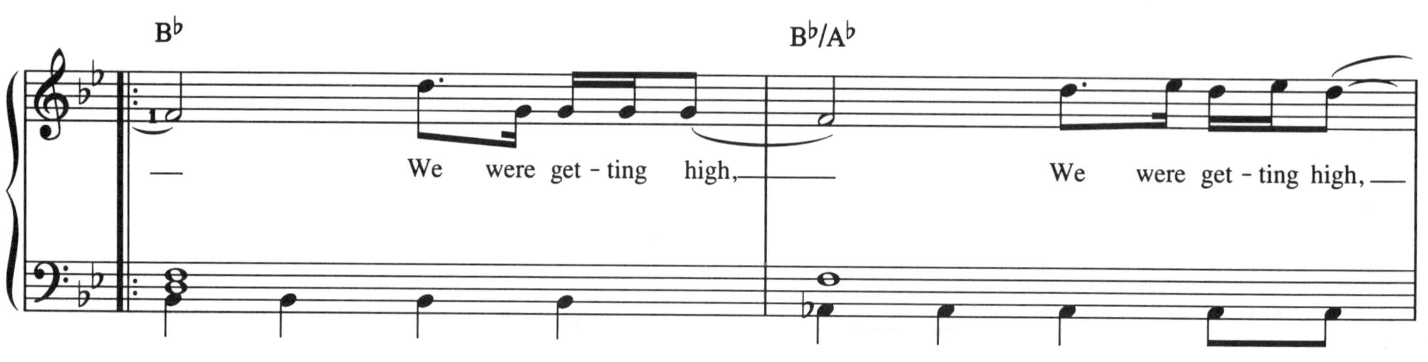

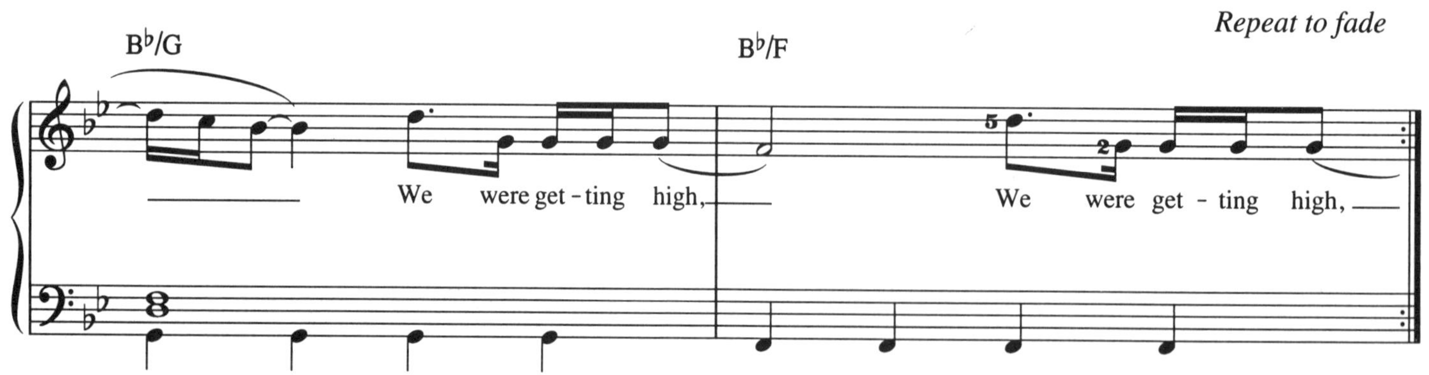

Verse 2:

How many special people change,
How many lives are living strange,
Where were you while we were getting high?
Slowly walking down the hall,
Faster than a cannon ball,
Where were you while we were getting high?

Cigarettes And Alcohol

Words & Music by Noel Gallagher

D
G D
G D G
You could wait for a life - time,
to spend your days in the sun -
D G D
- shine,
you might as well do the white line,
'cause when it
C G D C G
comes on top,
you got-ta make it hap - pen,
you got-ta make it hap-
D C G D C G
- pen,
you got-ta make it hap - pen,
you got-ta make it hap-

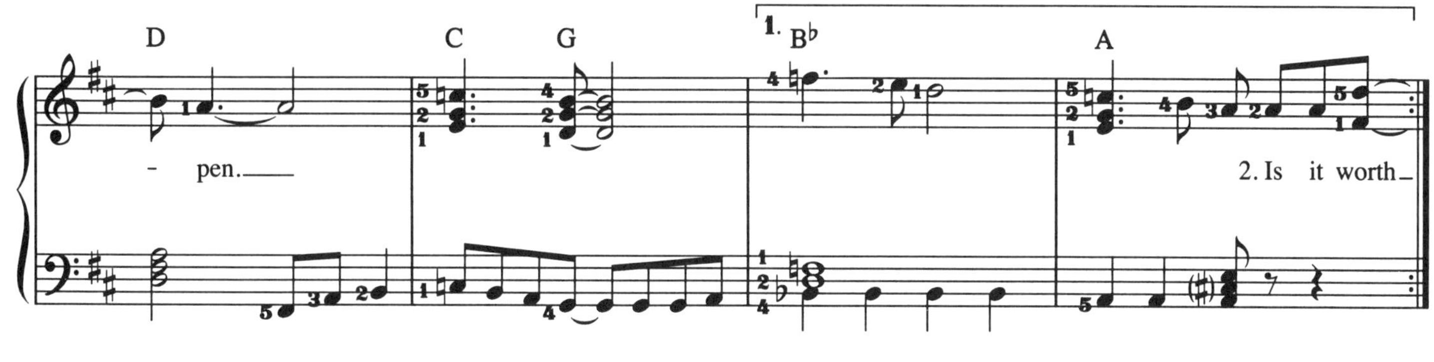

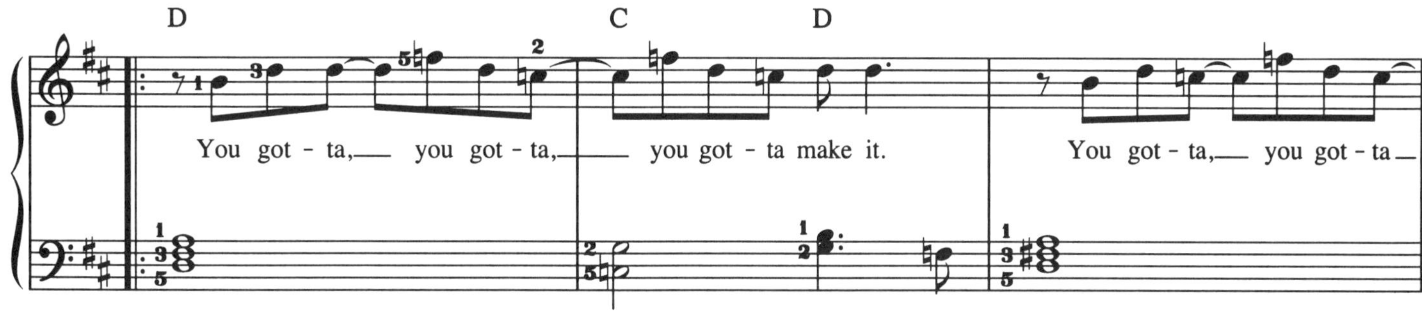

Verse 2:

Is it worth the aggravation
To find yourself a job
When there's nothing worth working for?
It's a crazy situation
But all I need
Are cigarettes and alcohol.

Don't Look Back In Anger

Words & Music by Noel Gallagher

Am E F G C Am G
but all the things that you've seen slow-ly fade a - way.
F Fm C F Fm
So I start a re-vo-lu-tion from my bed, 'cause you said the brains I had went to my
C F Fm C
head. Step out - side, sum - mer - time's in bloom,
G A♭
stand up be - side the fi - re - place, take that look from off your face,
G F G
you ain't ev - er gon - na burn my heart out.

Gsus4 G C G Am E
So Sal - ly can wait, she knows it's too late,
F G C
as { we're / she's } walk - ing on by { her / my }
C G Am E F G
To Coda
soul slides a - way. But don't look back in an - ger, I heard you
1. C G Am E F G C Am G
say.
2. D.S. al Coda
C Am G
say.
CODA
C Am G C G
say. So Sal - ly can wait,

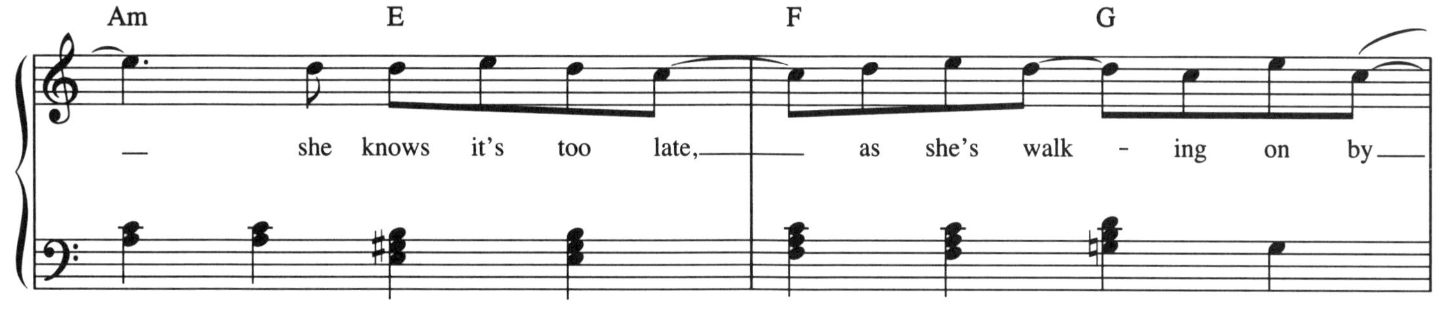

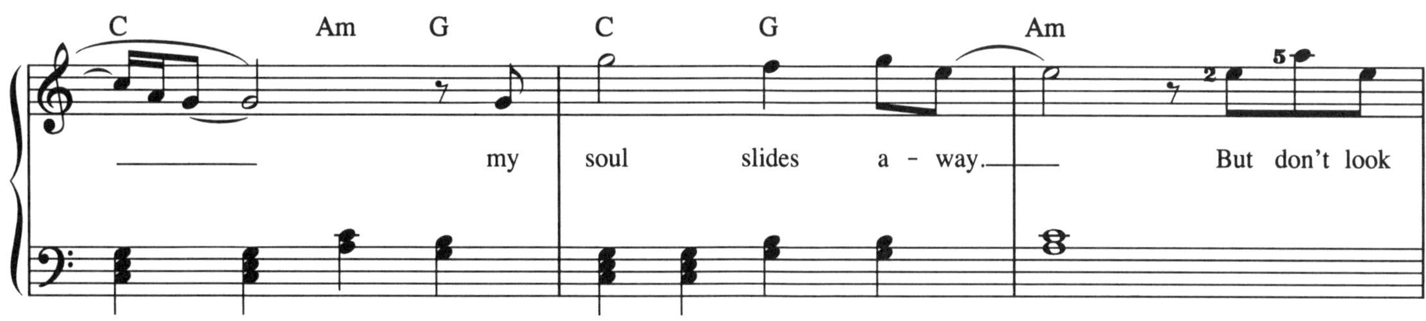

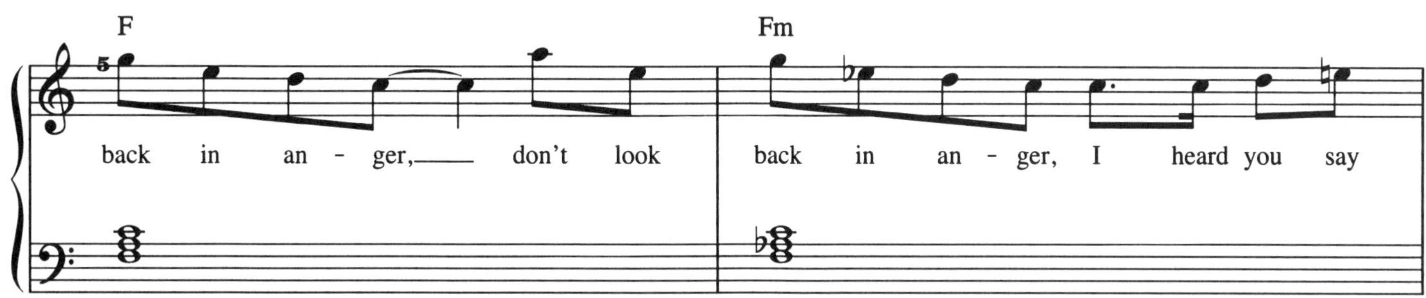

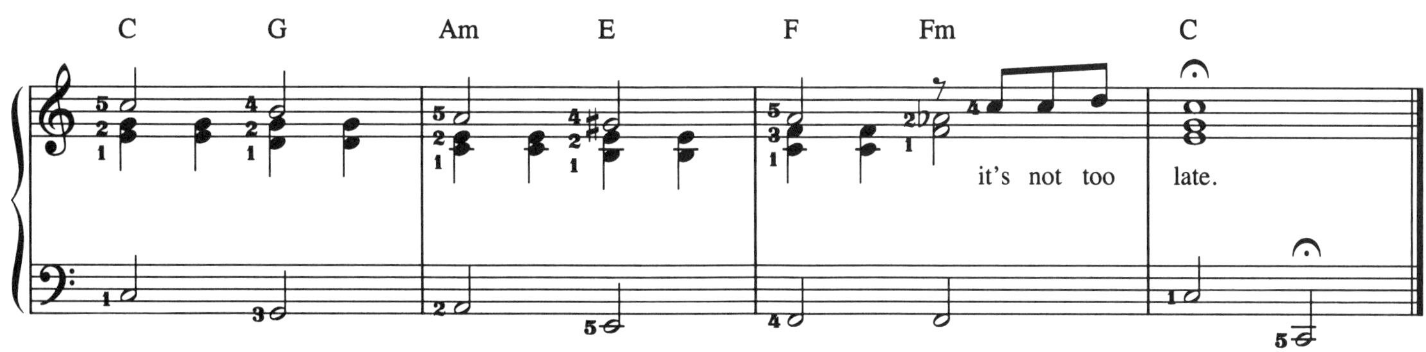

Verse 2:

Take me to the place where you go
Where nobody knows if it's night or day.
Please don't put your life in the hands
Of a rock 'n' roll band who'll throw it all away.

I'm gonna start a revolution from my head,
'Cause you said the brains I had went to my head.
Step outside, the summertime's in bloom,
Stand up beside the fireplace, take that look from off your face,
'Cause you ain't never gonna burn my heart out.

Hello

Words & Music by Noel Gallagher

(Includes an extract from Hello, Hello, I'm Back Again
Words & Music by Gary Glitter & Mike Leander)

C6
men - tions the wea - ther can
make or break your
day.
Am
No - bo - dy ev - er
seems to re - mem - ber
life is a game we
C6
G
E
Am
play.
We live in the
sha - dows and we
F7
G
C
C/B
had the chance and throw it a - way,
and it's
nev - er gon - na be the same,
Am
F
G
'cause the
years are fol - low - ing by
like the rain.
It's

C
C/B
Am
F
nev - er gon - na be the same
till the life
I knew comes to my
1.
D7
Am
Fmaj9
house and says hel- lo.
Am
Fmaj9
2. There
2.
D7
D
house and says
hel - lo
F
G
Am
hel - lo
hel- lo
F
G
Am
hel - lo

Verse 2:

There ain't no sense in feeling lonely,
They got no faith in you.
Well I've got a feeling you still owe me,
So wipe the shit from your shoes.

Live Forever

Words & Music by Noel Gallagher

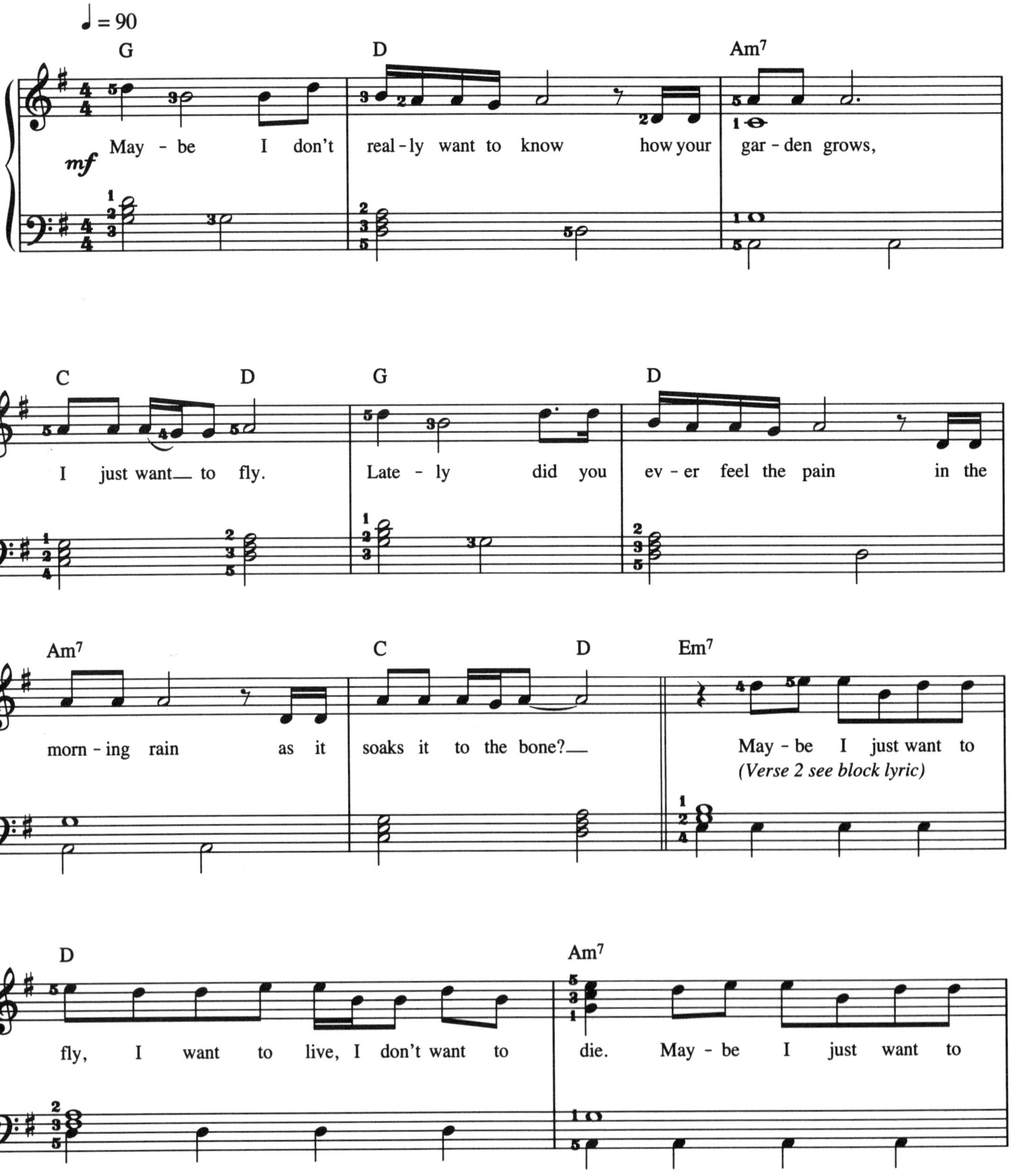

♩ = 90

G D Am7

mf May - be I don't real - ly want to know how your gar - den grows,

C D G D

I just want — to fly. Late - ly did you ev - er feel the pain in the

Am7 C D Em7

morn - ing rain as it soaks it to the bone? — May - be I just want to

(Verse 2 see block lyric)

C
D
Em7
breathe, may - be I just don't be -
lieve. May - be you're the same as
D
Am7
me, we see things they'll ne - ver
see, you and I are gon-na live for -
F
To Coda
1.
2.
G
ev- er,
I said
D
C
D
G
Em
D
Am7

C
D
Em
D

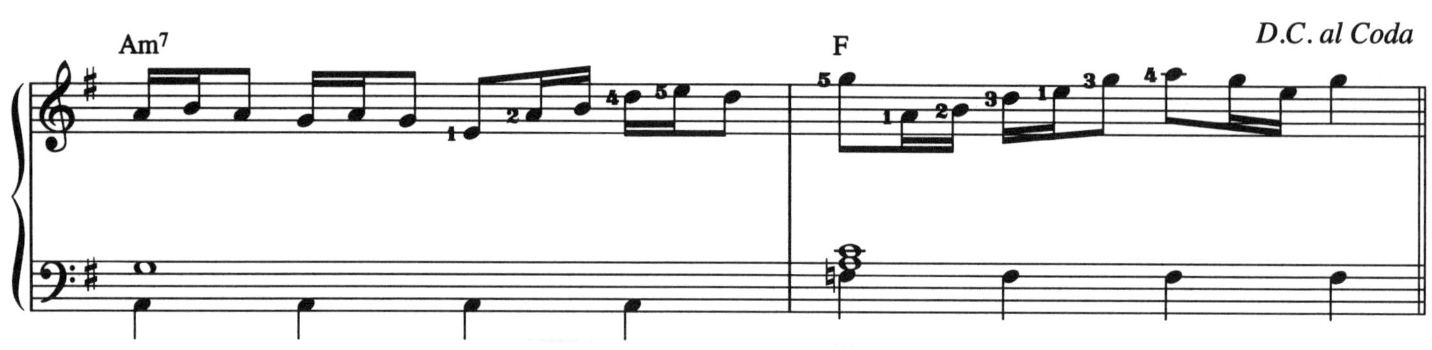
Am7
F
D.C. al Coda

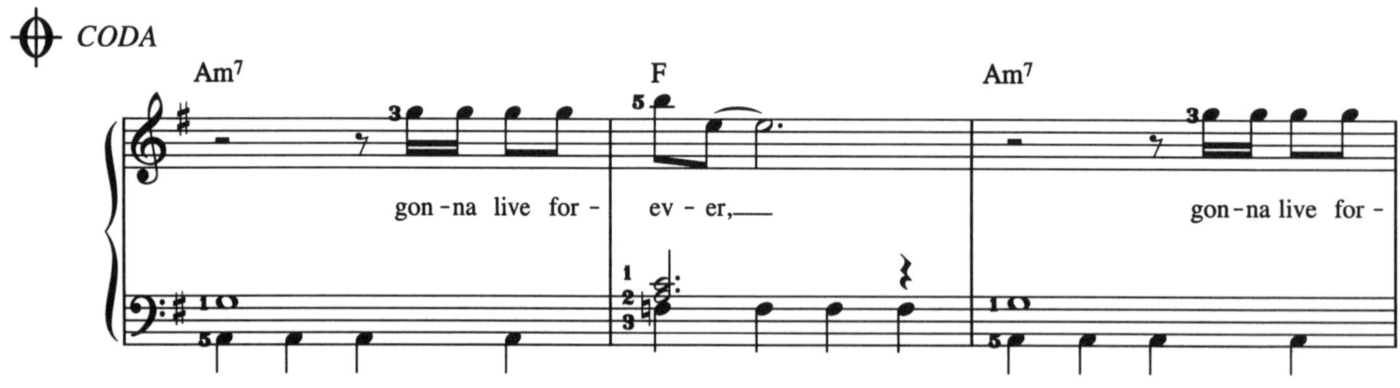
CODA
Am7
F
Am7
gon-na live for-
ev-er,
gon-na live for-

F
Am7
F
Am7
ev-er,
gon-na live for-
ev-er,
gon-na live for-

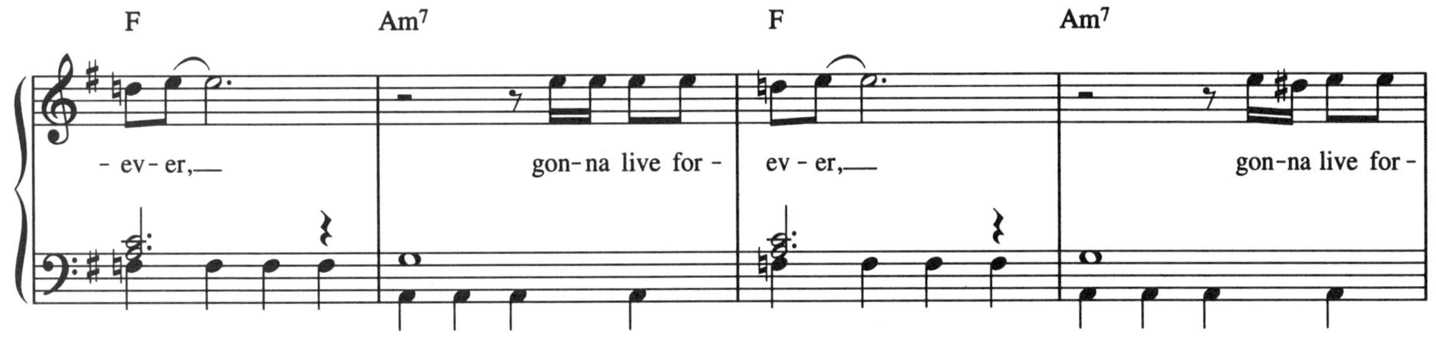

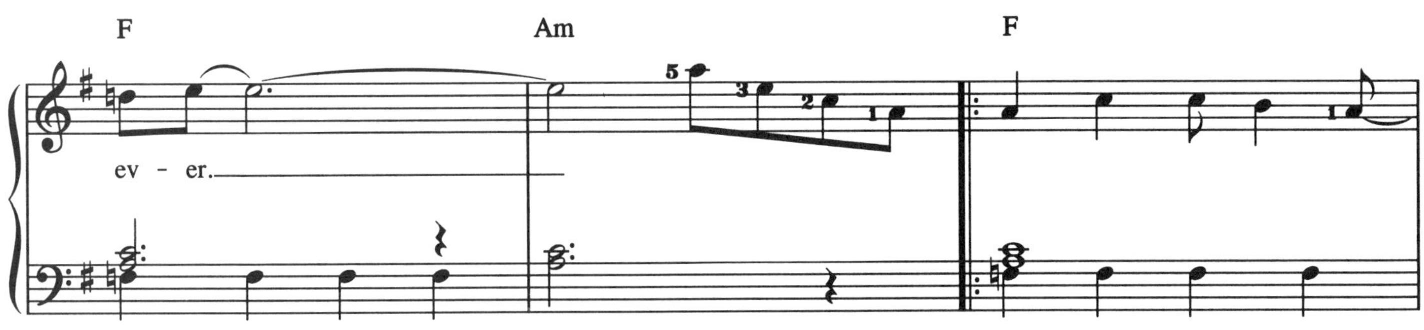

Verse 2:

Maybe I will never be
All the things that I want to be,
But now is not the time to cry.
Now's the time to find out
Why I think you're the same as me,
We see things they'll never see,
You and I are gonna live for ever...

Morning Glory

Words & Music by Noel Gallagher

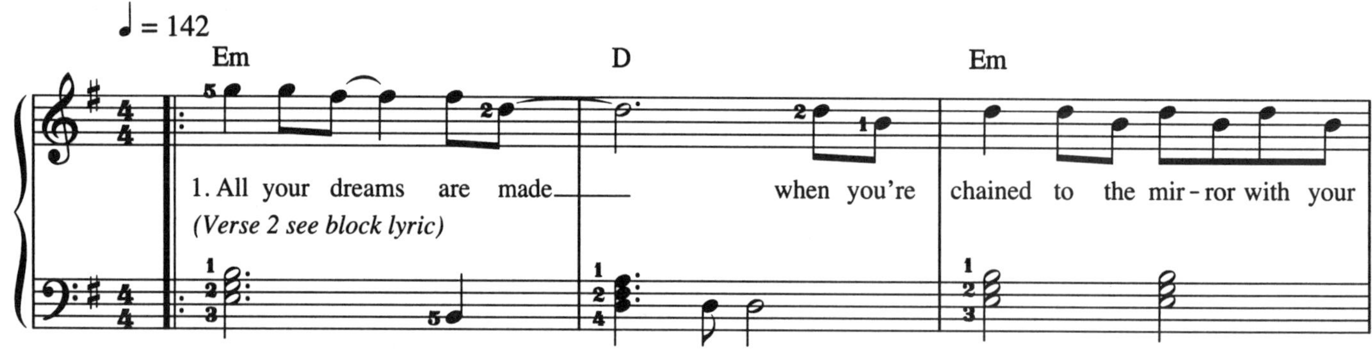

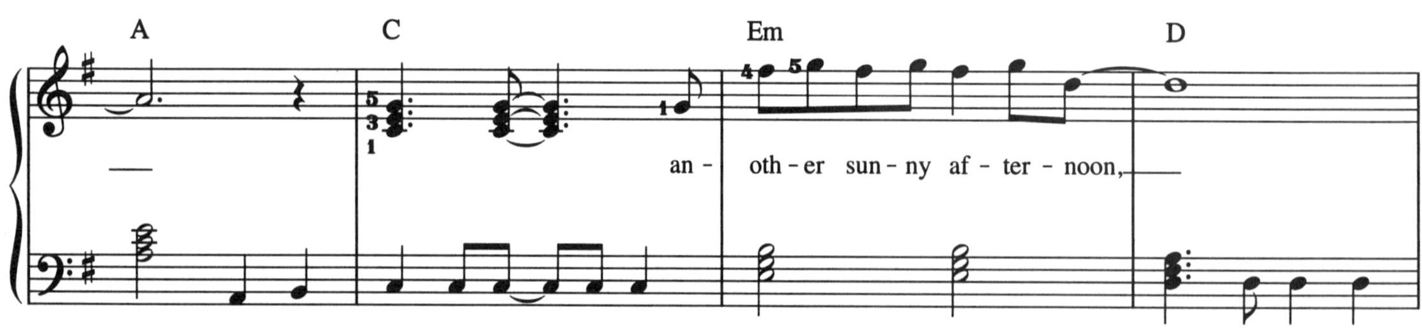

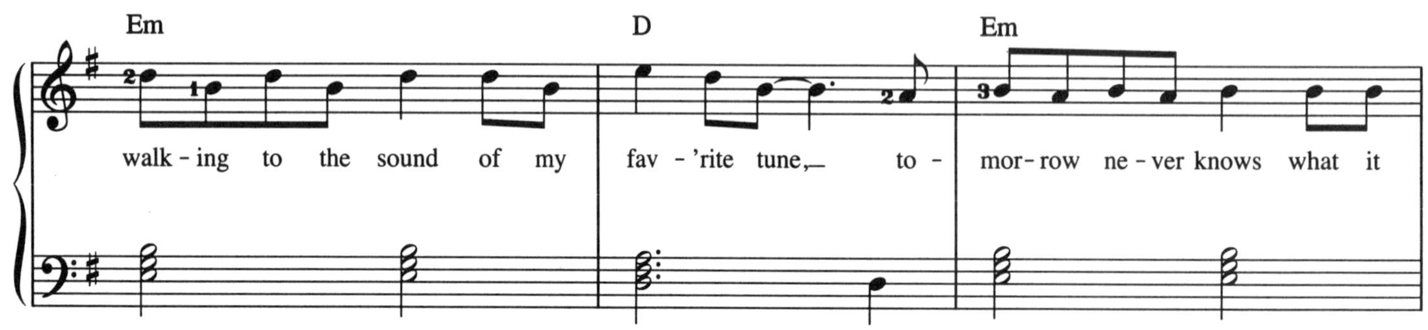

D
Am
C
does - n't know too soon.
D
C
D
Need a lit - tle time to wake up,
need a lit - tle time to wake
Cmaj7
D
Cmaj7
up, wake up,
need a lit - tle time to wake up,
D
B
need a lit - tle time to rest your mind, you
know you should so I guess
Em
D
A
C
you might as well.
What's the sto - ry morn -

Em
D
- ing glo - ry?
Well,
you
A
C
Em
D
need a lit-tle time to wake up, wake up,
well.
A
C
Em
D
What's the sto - ry morn - ing glo - ry?
Well,
you
A
C
need a lit-tle time to wake up, wake up.
1.
Em
3
3
3

Verse 2:

All your dreams are made
When you're chained to the mirror with your razor blade.
Today's the day that all the world will see
Another sunny afternoon,
I'm walking to the sound of my favourite tune,
Tomorrow doesn't know what it doesn't know too soon.

Roll With It

Words & Music by Noel Gallagher

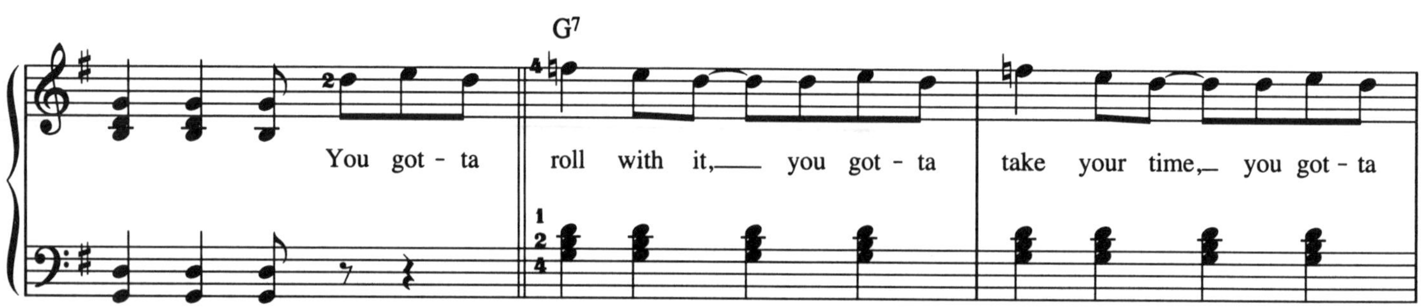

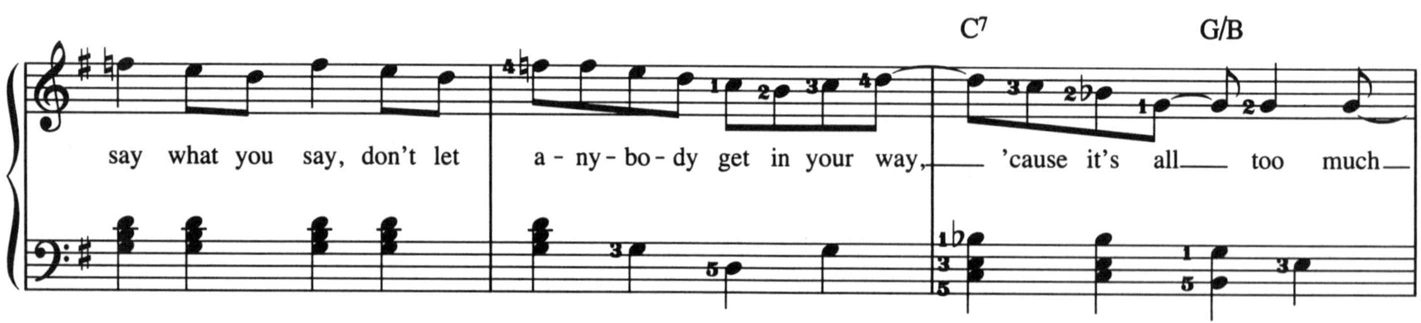

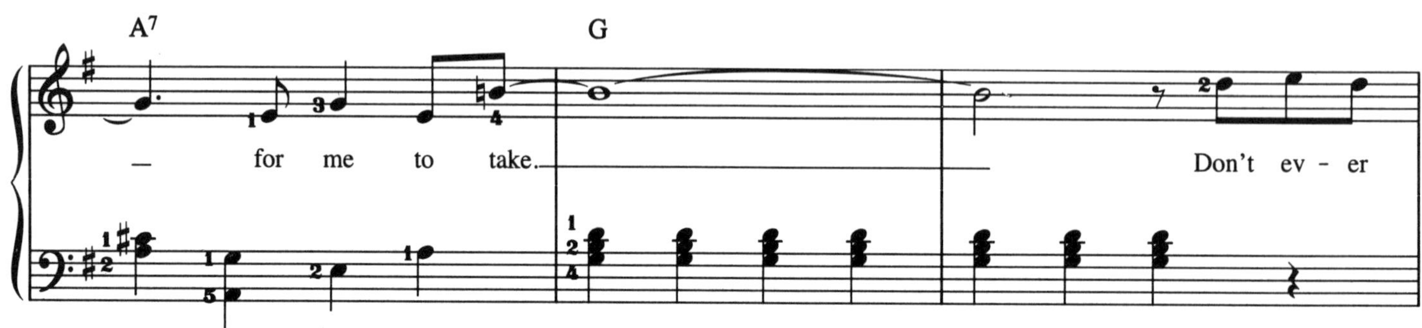

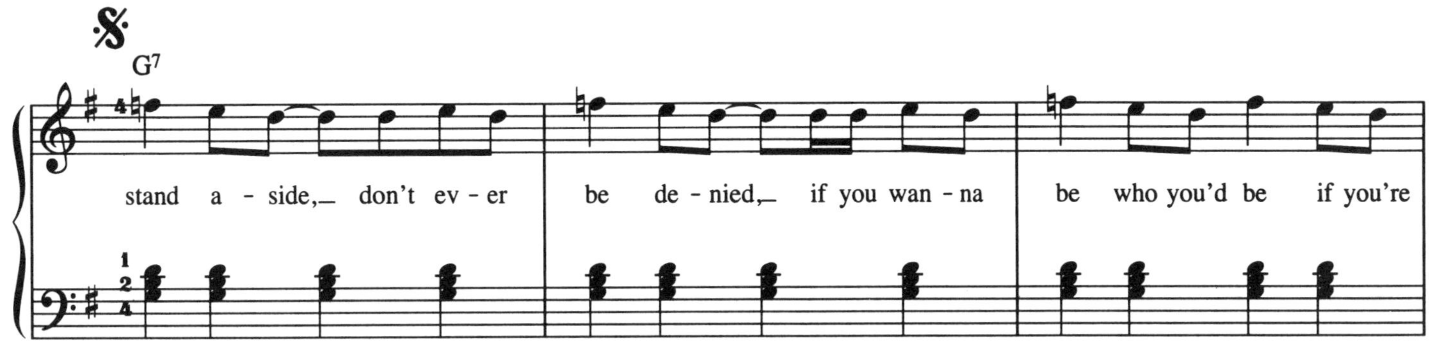
G7
stand a - side, don't ev - er
be de - nied, if you wan - na
be who you'd be if you're

C
G/B
Am7
com - in' with me. I
think I've got a feel - in' I've lost in - side; I
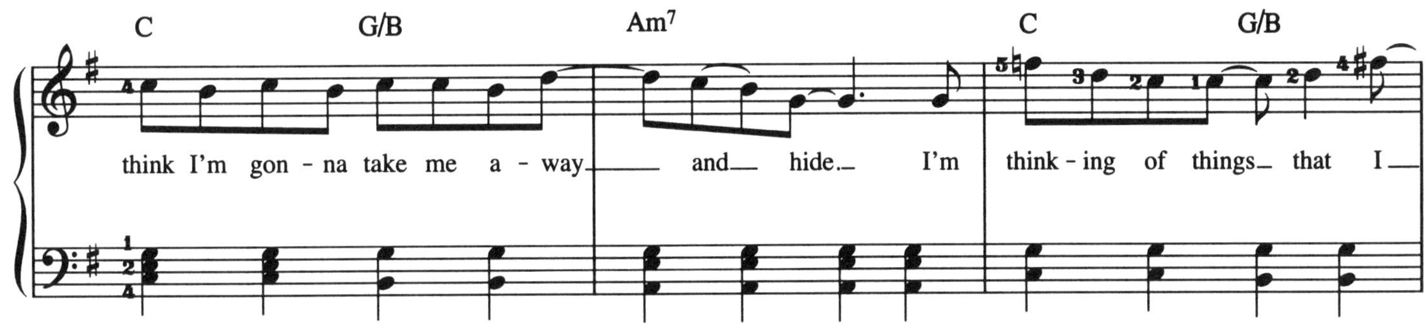
C
G/B
Am7
C
G/B
think I'm gon - na take me a - way and hide. I'm
think - ing of things that I

D
G
just can't a - bide.
I
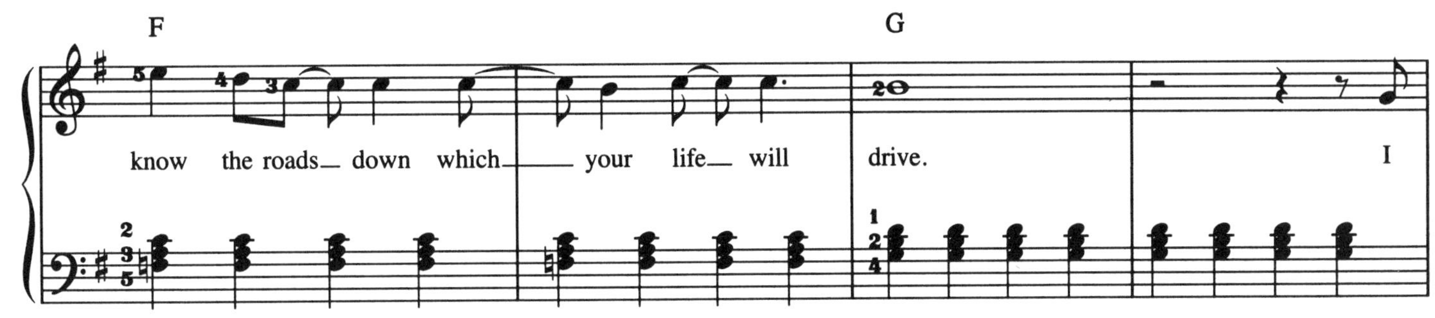
F
G
know the roads down which your life will drive.
I

F
G
find the key that lets you slip in - side.
F
G
Kiss the girl, she's not be - hind the door.
You
F
C
know, I think I re - cog - nise your face, but I've ne - ver seen you be - fore.
D
C
G
D
G
You got - ta roll with it, you got - ta
take your time, you got - ta say what you say, don't let an - y - bo - dy get in your way,

To Coda
C7
G/B
A7
G
'cause its all too much for me to take.
D.S. al Coda
Don't ev - er
CODA
Don't ev - er
stand a - side, don't ev - er be de - nied, if you wan - na be who you'd be if you're
com - in' with me. I
C
G/B
Am7
Play 8 times
think I've got a feel - ing I've lost in - side. (I)
C
G
Am7
Play 3 times
G

She's Electric

Words & Music by Noel Gallagher

D♭ E♭ F A Dm B♭
need more time. She's got a sis - ter and
F A Dm B♭ F A
God on - ly knows how I've missed her, and on the palm of her hand is a blis -
Dm B♭ D♭ E♭ F B♭
- ter and I need more time. And I
want you to know I've got my mind made up now,
Dm F F7
but I need more time.

B♭
And I want you to say, do you know what I'm say - ing?

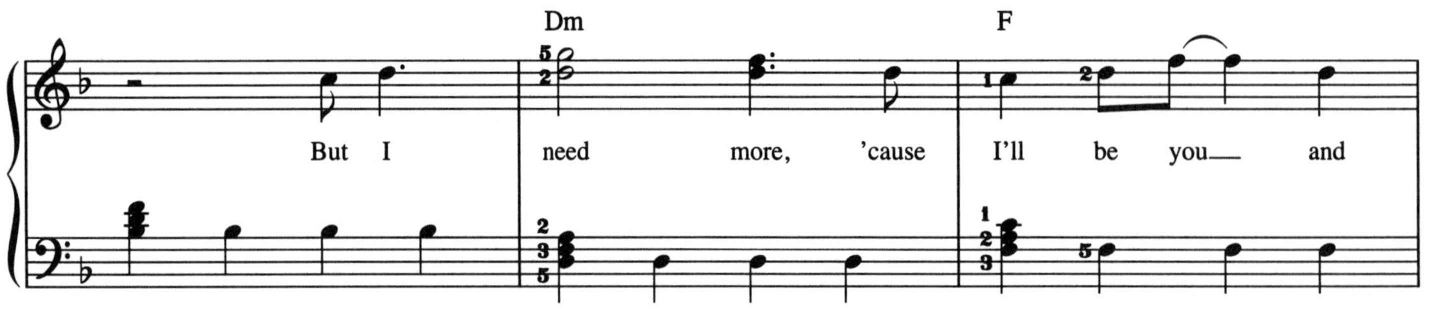
Dm
F
But I need more, 'cause I'll be you and

F7
Gm
you'll be me, there's lots and lots for us to see, lots and lots for

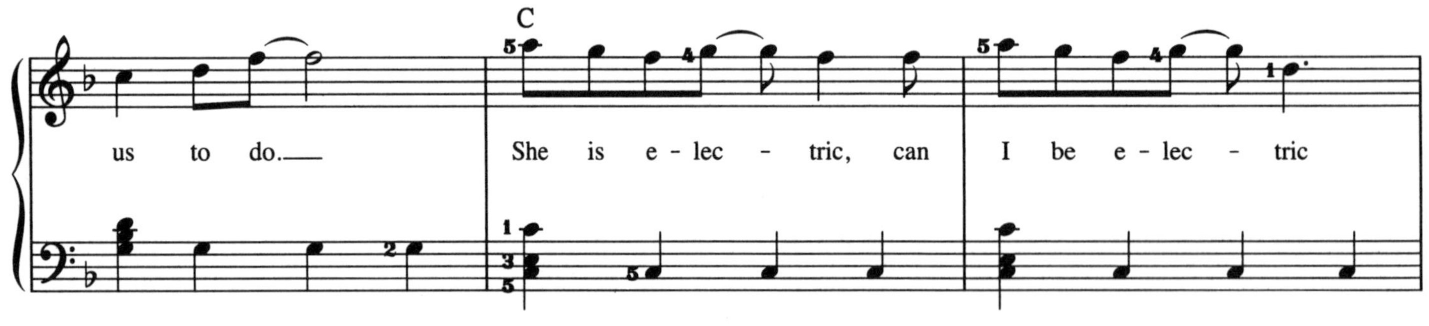
C
us to do. She is e - lec - tric, can I be e - lec - tric

1.
F
A
Dm
B♭
F
A
Dm
B♭
too?

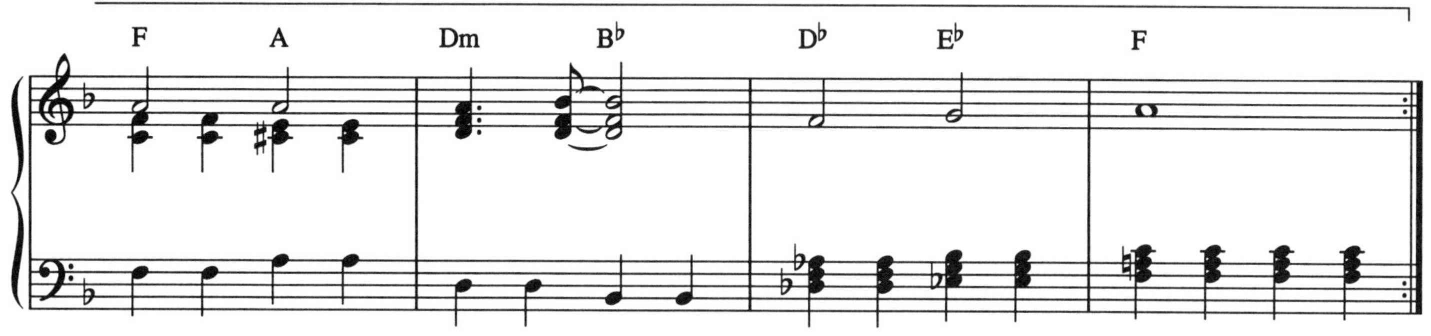

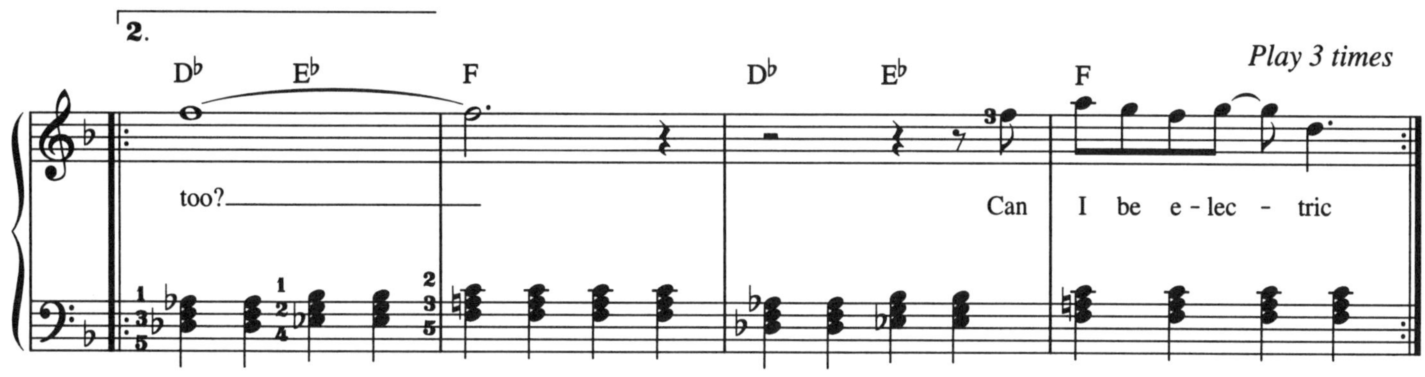

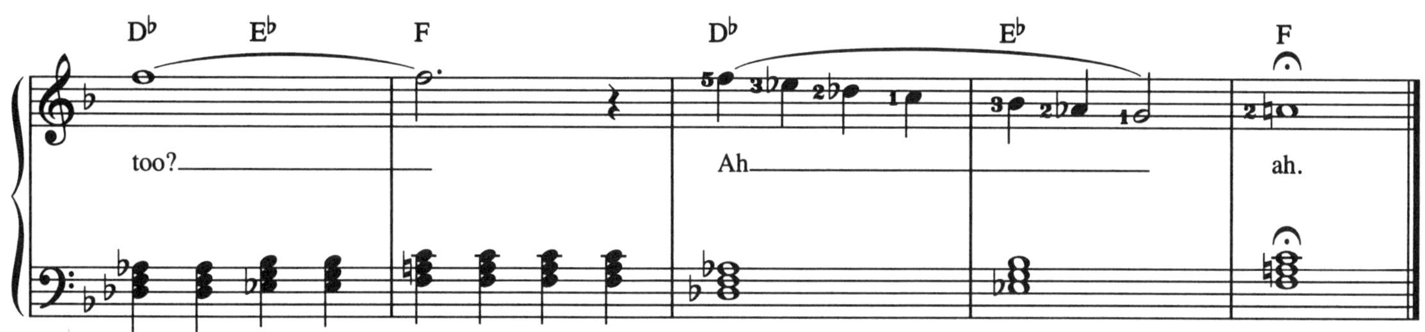

Verse 2:

She's got a brother,
We don't get on with one another,
But I quite fancy her mother
And I think that she likes me.
She's got a cousin,
In fact she's got 'bout a dozen.
She's got one in the oven
But it's nothing to do with me.

Some Might Say

Words & Music by Noel Gallagher

D
A
Em
hold sway over time.
Some might say
we will find
G
D
a bright - er day.
Some might
Em
C
G
say
we will find
a bright - er day.
'Cause I've been
D
G
Em
G
stand-ing at the sta-tion, in
need of ed - u - ca - tion in the
D
G
Em
D
G
rain.
You
made no pre - pa - ra - tion

Em G D G Em G
for my re - pu - ta - tion once a - gain. The
D G Em G
sink is full of fish - es 'cause she's got dir - ty dish - es on the
D G Em G D G
brain.
It was ov - er - flow - ing gent - ly, but
And my dog's been itch - ing,
Em G D G
it's all el - e - men - tary my friend.
itch - ing in the kitch - en once a - gain.
1. Em G F♯m
F C A

Repeat to fade

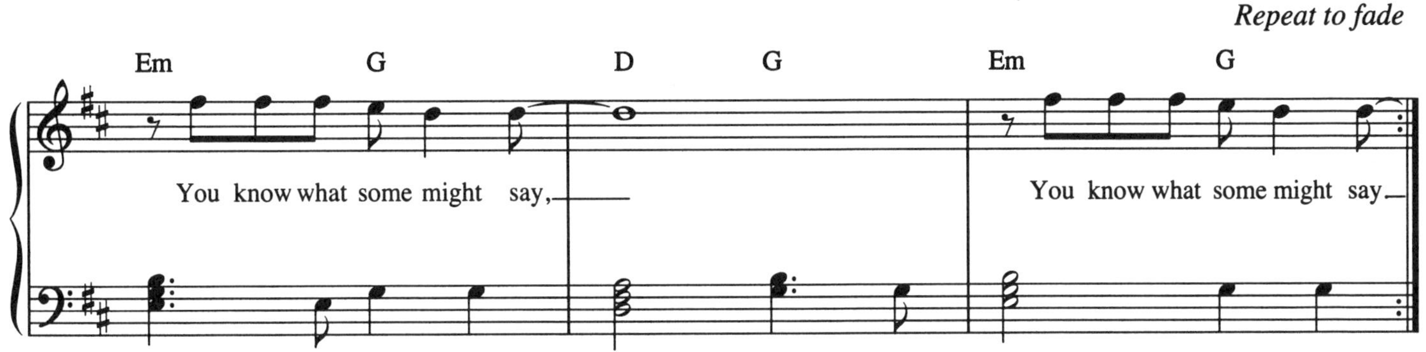

Verse 2:

Some might say they don't believe in heaven,
Go tell that to the man who lives in hell.
Some might say you get what you've been given,
If you don't get yours I won't get mine as well.

Supersonic

Words & Music by Noel Gallagher

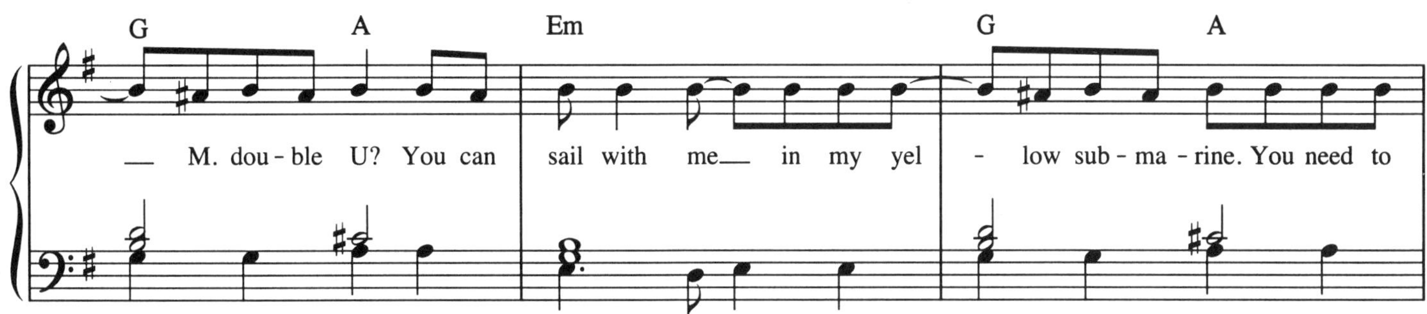
G A Em G A
— M. double U? You can sail with me — in my yel - low sub - ma - rine. You need to

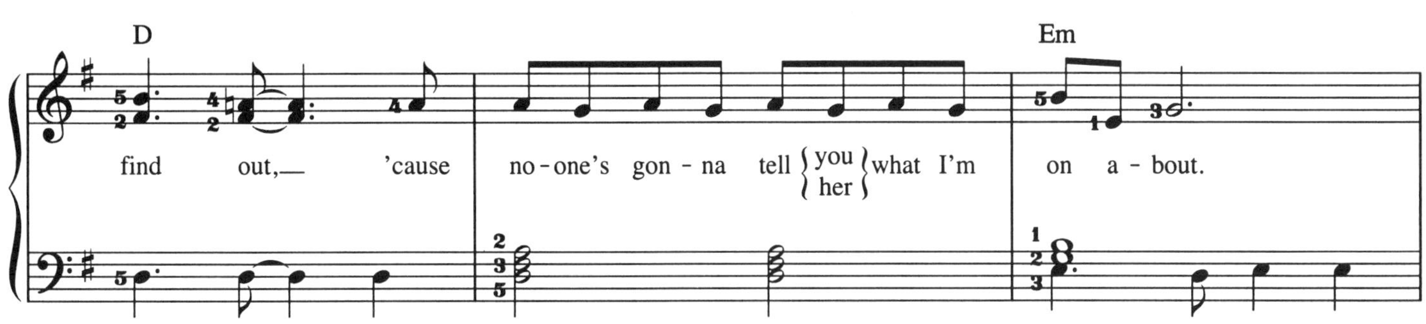
D Em
find out, — 'cause no - one's gon - na tell { you her } what I'm on a - bout.

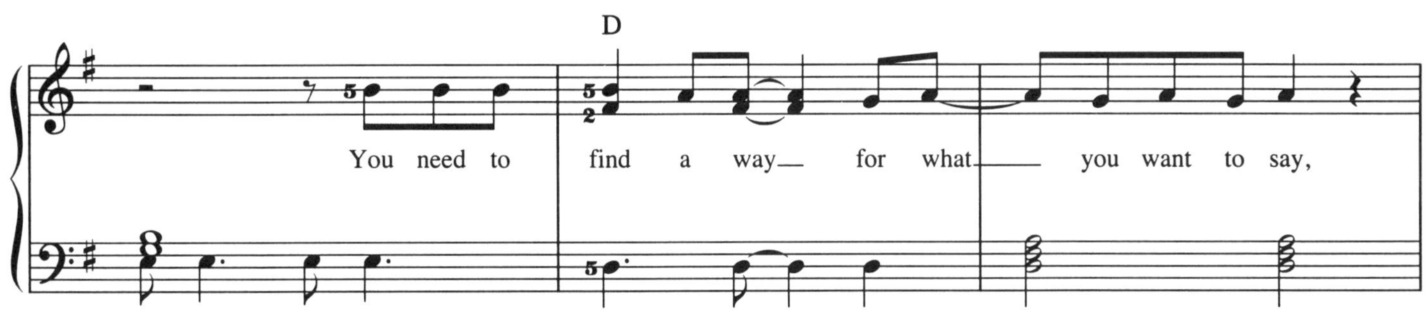
D
You need to find a way — for what — you want to say,

B7 C G
but be - fore — to - mor - row, 'cause my friend said — he'd take —

Em
C
G
D
Em
— you home,— he sits in a cor - ner all—— a - lone.—

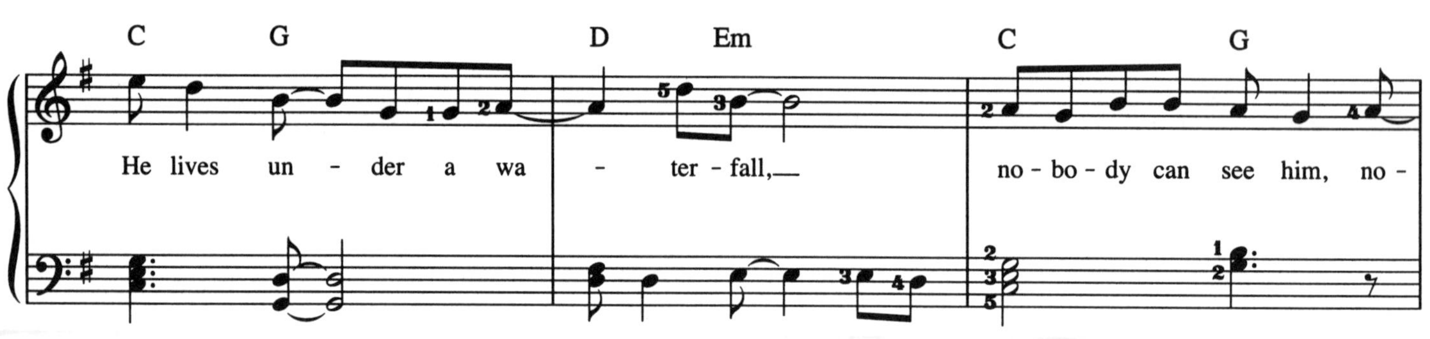
C
G
D
Em
C
G
He lives un - der a wa - ter - fall,— no - bo - dy can see him, no -

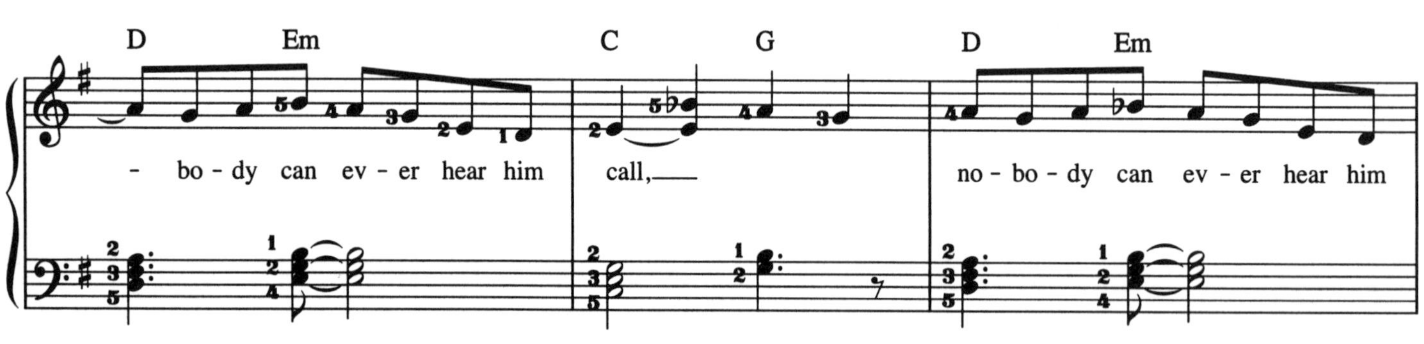
D
Em
C
G
D
Em
- bo - dy can ev - er hear him call,— no - bo - dy can ev - er hear him

C
G
D
Em
C
G
D
Em
call.—

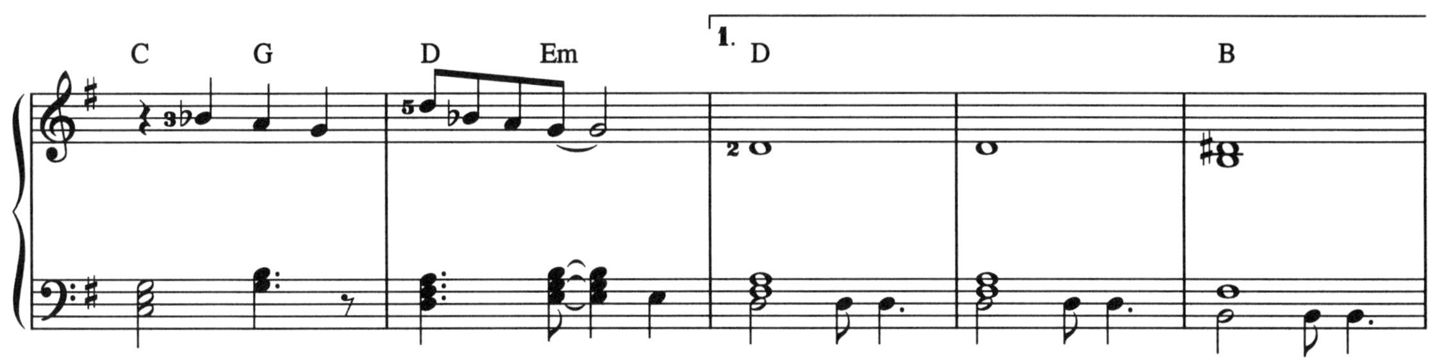

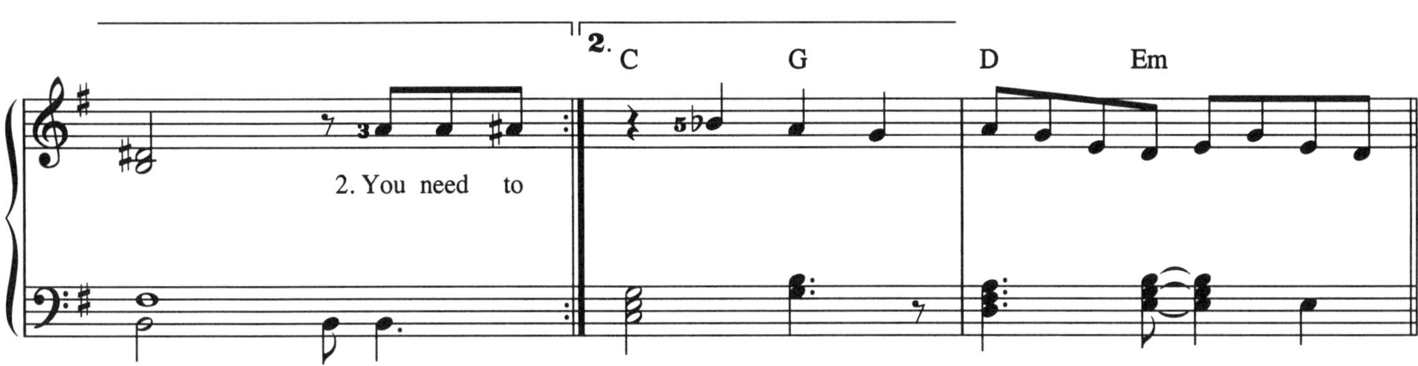

Verse 2:

You need to be yourself,
You can't be no one else.
I know a girl call Elsa,
She's into Alka Seltzer.
She sniffs it through a cane
On a supersonic train.

And she makes me laugh,
I got her autograph.
She done it with a doctor
On a helicopter,
She's sniffing in her tissue
Selling the Big Issue.

And she finds out...

Wonderwall

Words & Music by Noel Gallagher

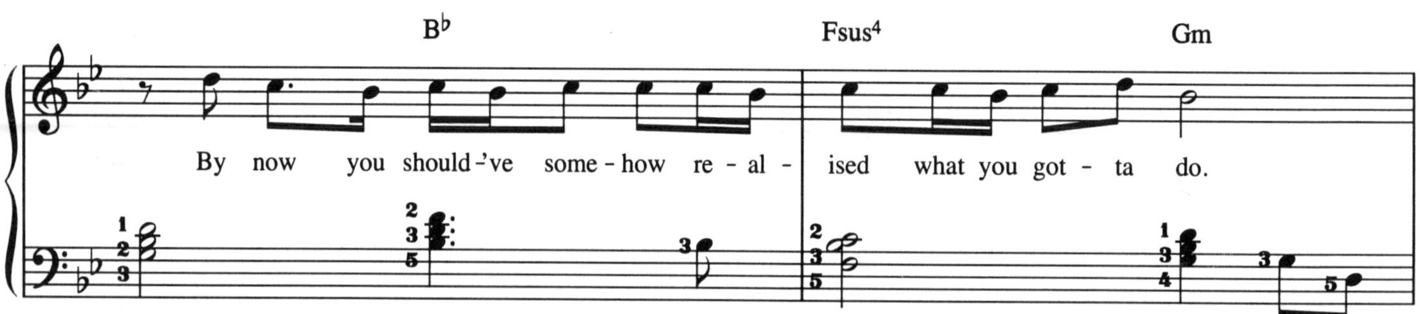

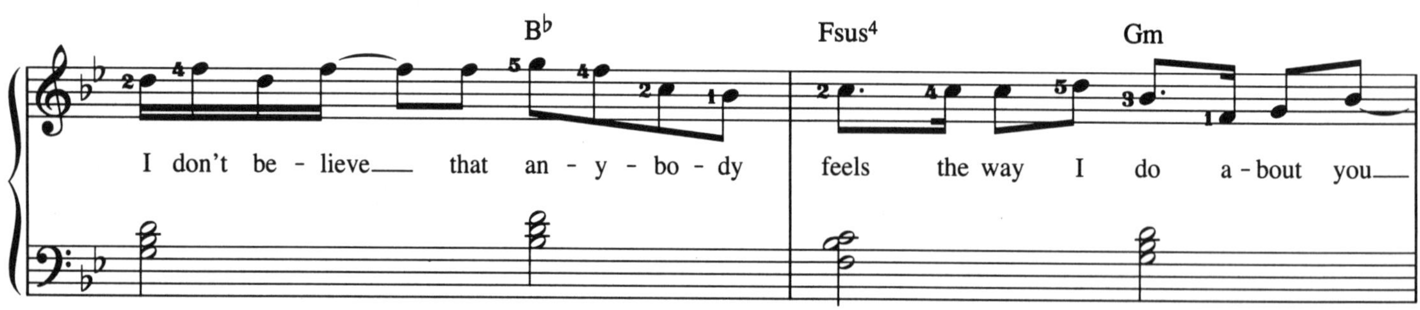

Fsus4 Cm7 Gm B♭
fi - re in your heart is out. I'm sure you've heard it all be-fore but you
Fsus4 Cm7 Gm B♭
ne-ver real-ly had a doubt. I don't be - lieve that an - y - bo - dy
Fsus4 Cm7 Gm B♭ Fsus4 Cm
feels the way I do a-bout you now. And
E♭ Fsus4 Gm E♭ Fsus4
all the roads we have to walk are wind - ing and all the lights that lead us there are
Gm E♭ Fsus4 B♭ Gm
blind-ing. There are ma-ny things that I would like to say to you but I don't know

Cm
how,
be - cause
I said
E♭
Gm
may - be
B♭
Gm
you're gon - na be the one that
E♭
Gm
saves me,
B♭
Gm
and af - ter all
E♭
Gm
B♭
Gm
you're my won - der -
E♭
Gm
wall.
1.
B♭
B♭6
2.
B♭
Gm
I said
E♭
Gm
may - be
B♭
Gm
you're gon - na be the one that
E♭
Gm
saves me,
B♭
Gm
and af - ter all

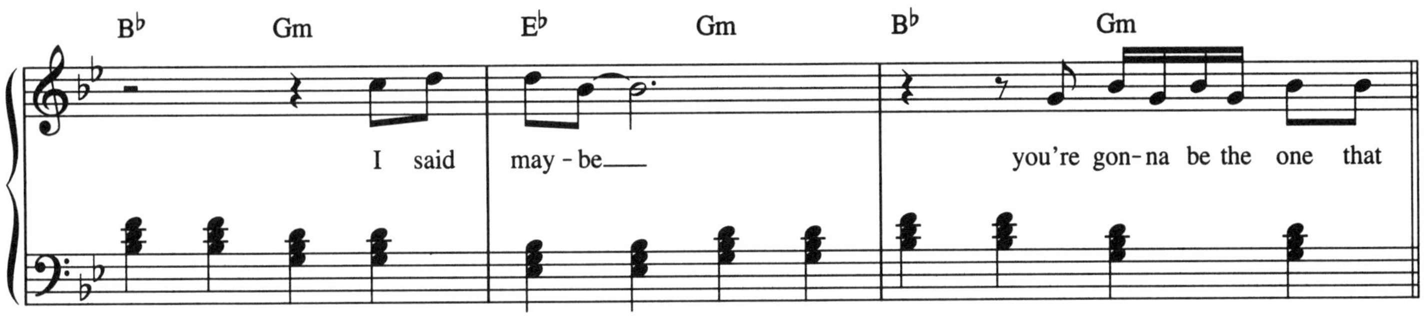

Verse 2:

Today was gonna be the day
But they'll never throw it back to you.
By now you should've somehow
Realised what you're not to do.
I don't believe that anybody
Feels the way I do
About you now.

And all the roads that lead you there were winding
And all the lights that light the way are blinding.
There are many things that I would like to say to you
But I don't know how.

The Beatles

Enya

Phil Collins

Van Morrison

Bob Dylan

Sting

Paul Simon

Tracy Chapman

Eric Clapton

Pink Floyd

New Kids On The Block

Bringing you the words

All the latest in rock and pop. Plus the brightest and best in West End show scores. Music books for every instrument under the sun. And exciting new teach-yourself ideas like "Let's Play Keyboard" - in cassette/book packs, or on video. Available from all good music shops.

Bryan Adams

Tina Turner

Elton John

Bee Gees

Whitney Houston

AC/DC

and music

Music Sales' complete catalogue lists thousands of titles and is available free from your local music shop, or direct from Music Sales Limited. Please send a cheque or postal order for £1.50 (for postage) to:

Music Sales Limited
Newmarket Road,
Bury St Edmunds,
Suffolk IP33 3YB

Buddy

Five Guys Named Moe

Les Misérables

West Side Story

Phantom Of The Opera

Show Boat

The Rocky Horror Show

Bringing you the world's best music.